*For Betty Smith, Colin Thomas
and Norma Jean.*

A round of "up-paws" for *Badger the Mystical Mutt*

"*Pitch-perfect subtlety and wit.*"
Shari Low, The Daily Record

"*Using Badger books is an excellent way of opening communication channels with how your child gets on at school.*"
Missing Sleep

"*There are some underlying morality themes that should allow vigorous class discussions*"
Stephen King, The School Librarian Magazine

"*I have to say I just love these books; they are written so well and sweep you up in tales of chaos, mayhem and fun, with a little bit of magic.*"
BFK Books

"*Kids' book takes world by storm.*"
The Scottish Sun

"*A moving and joyful story, which warmed the heart of this cynical old journalist.*"
That's Books

"*First-time winner.*"
The Evening Times

"*A toast-loving, magical hound, who has been winning fans in book shops, libraries and schools across Scotland.*"
The List

"*A charming and very funny children's story.*"
Diana Cooper

"*McNicol & Jackson have created a charming new book character; a toast-crunching hound named Badger.*"
Aye Write, Glasgow's Book Festival

"*A truly magical story, which has all the hallmarks of a future children's classic!*"
Ursula James

"*A magical 21st-century narrative, which will delight and inspire folk of all ages.*"
Alex Lewczuk, Southside Broadcasting

"*The toast-crunching, spell-muffing Badger the Mystical Mutt is a delightful, madcap, magical character, who worms his way into your affections.*"
Maggie Woods, MotorBar

"*Badger the Mystical Mutt is the coolest doggie around, and in his brilliant stories he helps young kids understand their world and believe in themselves and their ambitions.*"
Vegetarian Living Magazine

Chapter One

It was two puffs of a dandelion clock to summer. In the lane, noisy clangs and bangs, dings and dongs, rustles and bustles could be heard from Badger the Mystical Mutt's garden. He was rummaging in his favourite plant pot to find the bits and pieces he needed for a very important spell; a spell to stop screeches and screams in nasty dreams; the all-important spell to conjure up a magnificent Dreamcatcher.

He dug out a rusty old bicycle bell and looked at it thoughtfully. "Nope, that won't work, too loud."

He peered back into the pot and tugged at an old wellie boot and a cricket bat. He shook his head and threw them both aside.

He had another delve, and spotted a shiny basketball ring. "Aha, this is looking better". Then he spied a ball of string and a tattered feather filled pillow.

"Splendid, these are *exactly* what I need to help Lennie with his nightmares... if I could only remember the spell."

He scratched his head, closed his eyes, thought really hard and then uttered the magic words:

"Feathers flutter to this ball of string,

Weave your web to the basketball ring.
Tickle the nightmares and give them laughter,
Make them cheery and happy ever after"

Badger stood back and waited. Sparkles of light twinkled around him as the feathers, the string and the basketball ring lifted up, twirled around and headed straight for him.

Out in the lane, the birds were watching their youngsters try to fly, the alley cats were lounging in the shade of the old oak tree, and all was well in the neighbourhood. All except for Lennie, the new leader of the gang. A little further along the lane, Lennie was undergoing a terrifying torture. He was trapped in a murky dungeon and was tied to a strange stretching contraption. His tail was being pulled at one end while a tin watering can drenched his head at the other.

In a dank corner, Pogo Paws and Pickle sniggered as they turned a huge creaky wheel. With each turn, a mallet thumped Lennie's snout, and his tail was yanked even further.

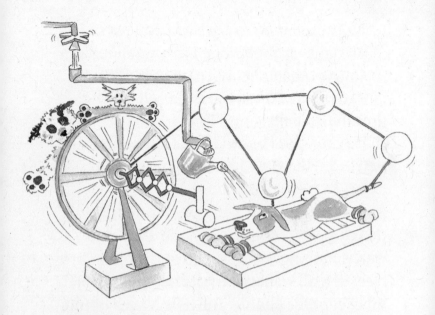

"Stop, please stop!" whimpered Lennie.

"Not until you admit you're a rubbish gang leader and resign immediately," shouted Pickle.

As the mallet struck him one more time, Lennie woke with a start.

He rubbed his nose and tried to wag his tail. All was fine. It had just been another of his horrible nightmares.

That's it, he thought. *I need to go and see Badger the Mystical Mutt, and find out if he's finished my Dreamcatcher.*

As Lennie trotted towards Badger's garden, he spotted Pogo Paws and Pickle in the distance. *Oh no,* he thought, *I've had quite enough of those two already today in that dreadful dream.*

He crouched behind the old oak tree and hid until they had disappeared out of sight. As he let out a huge sigh of relief, his nose caught the distinct whiff of a newly delivered p-mail. He sniffed the trail and read the message.

"Who is the Earl of Doodlepoppington?" he wondered aloud. "And why is he coming to visit Badger?"

He carried on to the famous crack in the fence at the bottom of Badger's garden, and peered through. He saw his friend in a bit of a fankle.

There were feathers everywhere. Badger was flat on his back with his bottom wedged in the basketball ring, and string strung from all angles.

"Oh, you look a bit tied up, Badger! Let me help," offered Lennie.

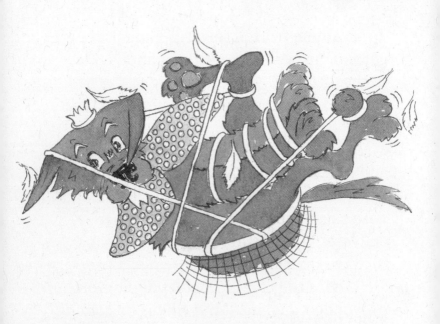

"Ah yes. The spell didn't quite work, but it's getting there," said Badger sheepishly.

With feathers tickling his nose, he wiggled his bottom free of the basketball ring, and shook himself.

Lennie chuckled and said: "I have a message for you. I just picked up a p-mail from the Earl of Doodlepoppington. He's coming to see you. Do you know him?"

"Doodles?" groaned Badger "Yes, I'm afraid I do. He's my distant cousin, and the rogue of the family. I wonder what he wants."

"Is he posh? He sounds posh?"

"He thinks he is. He lives with his father, the Duke, in a stately kennel in Upper Barkingford. His dad is a luxury doghouse developer, and a dastardly dealer. He's due to retire soon, and Doodles is set to take over."

"Gosh, that does sound posh, but I wouldn't swap where we live now for a stately kennel. I love it on the lane. If only I could get Pogo Paws and Pickle to be nicer..." Lennie sighed.

"I know. I love it on the lane too. Home is where the heart is, after all, and there's a lot of kindness around here. Not counting Pogo Paws and Pickle, obviously," said Badger. "I'm sure that the reason you're having nightmares is because you're worrying about being gang leader," he added.

"I never wanted to be the leader. Pogo Paws and Pickle get up to mischief *all* the time, and they insist on me joining in. I'm fed up with them both," grumbled Lennie.

"Well, maybe the Earl will distract them when he visits. Did he say when he's arriving?"

"Later today, I think."

"Yikes! I'd better get this place tidied up then," said Badger, looking at the feathery mess in his garden.

"Badger, just one thing... when do you think the Dreamcatcher will be ready? I've just had another nightmare, and this time Pogo Paws and Pickle were really horrible."

"Oh Lennie, I've got the feathers, I've got the ring and I've got the string, but I still need one other thing. In the meantime, try this under your pillow at night. Or sniff it whenever you feel upset."

Badger gave Lennie a small bag filled with calming lavender and camomile.

"Thanks, Badger, and good luck with

your visitor. I'm sure he can't be all bad if he's related to you," said Lennie.

"If only that were true!" sighed Badger.

As Lennie slipped through the crack in the fence and wandered up the lane, he took a deep breath and sniffed his little bag of calm. But when he rounded the corner, he bumped smack-bang into Pogo Paws and Pickle.

"Did you get the p-mail about the Earl?" yelled Pogo Paws.

"Who exactly *is* this Earl of Doodlepoppington anyway?" snarled Pickle.

"I know!" said Lennie triumphantly. "He's Badger's cousin, and by all accounts, he's a bit of scoundrel."

"Oh really?" glowered Pickle. "Being a scoundrel is *our* job. Who does he think he is, coming on to our patch? We'll sort him out, and show him who's who."

"*And* tell him whose territory this is," added Pogo Paws.

Pickle looked at Pogo Paws and said, "Hang on a minute. That's our *leader's* job."

They both looked expectantly at Lennie.

"So what's the plan then?" asked Pickle.

"Erm... I need to think about that," jittered Lennie.

"Well, you better think about it fast, because he's arriving soon. We'll meet you here at dusk, and you'd better come up with something, or else you're not fit to call yourself our leader," snarled Pickle.

Pickle spied the little bag that Lennie was clutching.

"What's *that*?" she pointed a paw in his direction.

"Just something to help me sleep better" said Lennie.

"You're so namby-pamby, Lennie." Pickle lunged at the little bag and tore it apart. The lavender and camomile scattered in the lane as Pogo Paws and Pickle ran off sniggering.

Lennie was left trembling and scrambled about to pick up whatever sprigs were left of the relaxing herbs.

He sat alone in the middle of the lane with his heart pounding. His breathing was fast and shallow.

"This is a nightmare, and I'm still awake," he panicked. "They want me to show this Earl who's boss. How can I do that when I don't even want to *be* the boss?"

Chapter Two

In Badger's garden, there was much flurry and fluster. The Mystical Mutt had crafted a baa-baa-flick — a multi-coloured duster — from all of the feathers. Now, he was rushing around trying to make everything just so for his cousin's arrival. He had polished his plant pot, dusted down the sundial and cleared the shed of cobwebs.

The fluffiest blankets were in his bed and he had changed the water in his drinking bowl. His

neckerchief was freshly ironed and his nails were clipped. He was even willing to share his higgledy-piggledy tower of toast. Standing back to inspect his handiwork, he felt very pleased with himself. He eyed the tower of toast hungrily, and decided he deserved a few slices now. After all, he'd worked very hard cleaning and tidying.

As he munched on his snack, he heard the distant pomp of an approaching fanfare. Badger peered out into the lane and saw all the birds lined up along the fence, with their chests puffed out in salute. As the fanfare drew nearer, the alley cats emerged to see what all the fuss was about. Badger stood to attention as a long elegant nose came into view, followed by the noble swish of an Afghan hound.

The Earl of Doodlepoppington had arrived.

"Greetings, dear fellow," said the Earl.

"Hi, Doodles," answered Badger.

"Ssssshhhh! Don't call me Doodles. I shall be addressed by my full title at all times," said the Earl snootily.

"Okay, Doodles. Come on in to my gracious abode."

The Earl cringed as he stepped through the crack in the fence and into Badger's garden.

"Well, I suppose this will have to do," he sneered. "It's only for a short time. My work here should be speedy enough."

"Your work?" enquired Badger. "I thought this was just a visit."

"Ah, indeed, dear boy, a bit of business and er ..." the Earl raised a disdainful eyebrow, "... and a bit of pleasure."

"What kind of business?" asked Badger, suspiciously.

"Well, you know, of course, that my father is soon to hand over the business to me, so I must investigate potential sites for development," boasted his cousin. "But enough of that just now. First, let's feast and I'll show you my plans later."

Once they'd had their toast and Badger had updated his cousin on all his adventures, he told him about Lennie's problems with his nightmares and the gang.

The Earl dismissed Badger's worries and rolled out the drawings for his latest project: a development of bespoke luxury doghouses.

Badger's eyes widened at the plans for kennels designed for over-pampered pups. They included fur-lined, temperature-controlled beds, automated food and water dispensers, day lounges, spa baths and paw-pad entry systems.

"Toastastic, Doodles! I've never seen anything like it. Where are you planning this?" asked Badger excitedly.

The Earl chuckled, tapped his nose with his paw and said, "Closer than you think, Badger boy. Now, tell me more about this gang. Do they actually *live* on the lane?"

Meanwhile, the lane shook with the rumble of heavy snoring. Lennie lay amidst the lavender and camomile in a deep, deep sleep. His paws twitched, his tail swished and his eyebrows wiggled from side to side in alarm.

He was stuck inside another of his nightmares, and this time he was at the seaside. But he wasn't running in the waves, or chasing a stick. He was lying very still upon the sand. His head was umbrella-shaped, and his paws had become trailing tentacles. Lennie had turned into a squidgy jellyfish.

Pogo Paws and Pickle sped towards him, with a giant bouncy beach ball. He started to quiver. Suddenly, Pickle threw the ball directly at him, and crushed his wobbly body into the sand. He squished about helplessly whilst Pogo Paws and Pickle aimed again, shouting gleefully:

"We've found you, so finders keepers, losers weepers. Try not to cry, Lennie while we splat you!"

As eight paws trampled closer to Lennie's terrified face, he let out an almighty yell: "Don't squash me, don't squash me!"

He jerked awake to see the alley cats looking at him quizzically. At their feet were the remains of a torn old beach ball.

"It's okay, Lennie. Playtime's over. We've scratched and burst this ball, so no more squashing for us today," answered the amused alley cats.

Lennie stood up and shook himself.

"Oh no, I must have been asleep for ages. It's almost dusk, and I still haven't come up with a plan to impress Pogo Paws and Pickle. The Earl needs to know that *we're* in charge of the lane."

He really needed the Dreamcatcher but, more importantly, he needed a plan. And Badger was his only hope. He headed straight for the Mystical Mutt's garden.

Chapter Three

The Earl of Doodlepoppington strolled along the lane with his notebook, pencil and tape measure. He measured up. He measured down. He calculated far. He calculated wide. In his notebook, he jotted this, and he jotted that. He set up his tripod and placed his very expensive camera on top. He clicked here. He snapped there. Suddenly, he heard the rattle of bin lids nearby.

"Come out!" he

commanded. "Show yourself! There's no point in hiding. I know you are there".

Two heads appeared from behind the bins: Pogo Paws and Pickle. They marched up to the Earl.

"You need permission to take pictures of the lane," said Pickle bossily.

"Do I indeed?" said the Earl. "And from *whom* should I seek this permission, pray tell?"

"Us! *We're* the gang and *we're* in charge of the lane," said Pickle assertively.

"Oh, *you're* the gang? Shouldn't I really be discussing this with your illustrious leader? Lennie, is it? The same Lennie who doesn't actually want to be your leader, and is having dreadful nightmares? Poor dear Lennie!" mocked the Earl.

Pogo Paws and Pickle looked at each other in shame.

"Perhaps I should consult with you two?" suggested the Earl. "You seem fairly streetwise, and can recognise a good deal when it's offered."

Pickle sneered. "What do you mean? This is *our* patch, and *you're* on it. So get off it, now!"

The Earl raised himself up to his full height and looked down his very long nose.

"Who's going to make me?"

"Us!" said Pogo Paws and Pickle together.

"You, and whose army?" scoffed the Earl, looking all around him. "Perhaps I should tell you my plans? I can assure you I will make it worth your while."

Pogo Paws and Pickle stepped closer and huddled in to hear what the Earl had to say.

Lennie arrived in Badger's garden in a panic. He found Badger busy setting out the bristles and brushes for his cousin's strict grooming regime.

Sorry to interrupt you, Badger. I really need your advice. It's about your cousin," pleaded Lennie.

"Doodles? What's he done?"

"Well, that's the thing. He hasn't done anything ... yet. But Pogo Paws and Pickle think I should see him off our patch. I've got to meet them and tell them what my plan is. What shall I do?" He sighed.

Badger scratched his head and said: "I'd be happy to see the back of him too. Now, let me think. Aha, I might just have the very thing. The Earl's prime concern is his grooming. He likes to show off his magnificent coat and long locks. What we need is something which will scupper that. So maybe I could magic up a flea?"

"A flea?" asked Lennie.

"Yes, a flea to make him flee." Badger chuckled.

He picked up a nearby crumb of toast and pulled a jam jar from his plant pot. He put the crumb inside the jar, then placed it very carefully in front of him. Lennie watched as sparkles of light twinkled around Badger.

His eyebrows twitched as he closed his eyes and said the rhyming spell:

"Take this single crumb of bread,
Give it a body and a head.
Make it bounce and make it jump,
Onto Doodlepoppington's rump.
Become a flea and make him scratch,
And send him packing from our patch."

Lennie and Badger both stepped back nervously hoping the spell had worked. Slowly, the crumb transformed into an energetic flea.

"Now," said Badger lifting up the jam jar and handing it to Lennie. "Take this, and go and meet Pogo Paws and Pickle. Tell them your plan. I think they'll be impressed."

"Amazing, Badger! Thank you so much. That should work a treat," said Lennie gratefully.

As he turned to go, he painfully remembered his nightmare from before. "How's it going with the Dreamcatcher, Badger? I had another nightmare earlier, and this time I was a jellyfish."

"That doesn't sound so terrifying, Lennie. Anything with the word 'jelly' in it can't be that bad!" said Badger licking his lips.

"Yes, but Pogo Paws and Pickle were about to squash me!"

"Ah!" agreed Badger. "Not so good. Okay, I need one final thing to complete your Dreamcatcher: a sprinkling of Jupiter's jewels can only be found in the Crystal Cave, and that involves a special trip. But I have something you could try in the meantime."

Badger searched in his plant pot and pulled out another jam jar filled with milk and cinnamon.

"You just need to warm it a little before drinking it, but it should keep those nightmares at bay in the short term."

"Thanks, Badger."

"Good luck with Pogo Paws and Pickle, Lennie."

Lennie trotted back up the lane with his two jam jars, to meet Pogo Paws and Pickle. He stood in front of them both triumphantly with his paws behind his back.

"I've sorted it, look!" He thrust a paw towards them, proudly showing the jam jar.

"Milk?" exclaimed Pogo Paws.

"What's that going to do exactly?" snapped Pickle.

"Oops, wrong one," said Lennie quickly, showing them the other jar.

Pogo Paws and Pickle peered through the glass.

"What's that?" asked Pogo Paws.

"It's a jumping flea, to make him flee our patch once and for all," said Lennie, feeling very chuffed.

"Ah, er, well done, Lennie. But actually, plans have changed," said Pickle.

"What do you mean? This is the perfect way to get rid of him," said Lennie.

"But we don't want to get rid of him now," said Pogo Paws.

"The Earl has offered us a job," said Pickle. "And in return, he's giving us a swanky new luxury doghouse to live in."

"What? Where? And what about me?" asked Lennie.

"What about you? You've not been much of a leader to us. Here's a new home for *you!*"

They dragged Lennie to the sandpit at the end of the lane and threw him in.

Pogo Paws and Pickle kicked up sand with their back legs until Lennie was covered right up to his neck.

They both ran off cackling. Lennie couldn't move an inch. He closed his eyes and hoped for a miracle.

Chapter Four

The searing rays of the sun beat down upon Lennie's head. He was so, so very thirsty. Inches away from his face, a scorpion scuttled. Out of the corner of his eye, he spied a snake slithering towards him. If he could have moved at all, he would have trembled. Suddenly, he felt the ground vibrate and looked into the haze. Coming straight towards him were two galloping camels. As they drew closer, Lennie scrunched up his eyes to focus. The riders were Pogo Paws and Pickle.

"Oh, my saviours! They've come at last to rescue me. And they've got water flasks too."

Pogo Paws and Pickle stopped abruptly in front of Lennie, and jumped off their camels.

"Am I glad to see both of you! Please can I have some water?" gasped Lennie.

Pogo Paws swung the water flask in front of Lennie's eyes.

"Are you thirsty Lennie?" he teased. "Before we let you drink, tell us where you've hidden the Crunchy Munchy Chewy Chops!"

"What are you talking about? I haven't got any Crunchy Munchy Chewy Chops," said Lennie.

"Oh, but I think you *do*," said Pickle.

"But I don't. Please can I just have some water?" begged Lennie.

Pickle grabbed the flask from Pogo Paws and giggled. "Of course you can, Lennie." She emptied out the flask on to the sand in front of him. The wet sand gurgled and frothed, and then started to shift around Lennie. Pogo Paws quickly poured another flask into the sand.

"This is called quicksand, Lennie, and if you're not quick, it will pull you under, and you'll sink without a trace," cackled Pickle.

Lennie's chin started to disappear into the clutching sand.

Tell us where the Chewy Chops are, and then we'll save you," growled Pogo Paws.

Lennie spluttered through a mouthful of sand. "I don't know where they are!"

Just then, he heard a voice. "Don't know where what are, dear chap?"

He opened his eyes nervously and looked up. It was pitch-black. Above him stood the Earl of Doodlepoppington. He was back in the sandpit in the lane and night had fallen.

"Phew, I'm not in the desert, it was another nightmare" sighed Lennie

"You are causing me a nightmare right now Lennie" said the Earl "this sandpit has to go".

"Has to go where? What do you mean?" asked Lennie.

"Go from here. It doesn't fit with my plans. It's an eyesore" said the Earl.

"What plans?" asked Lennie.

"My plans for developing the lane into luxury kennels, of course," he replied.

"What? Here? But what about everyone who lives here already?" asked Lennie in alarm.

"What about them?" scoffed the Earl. "They'll simply move on. Surely one cardboard box is much the same as another? Anyway, I have no wish to be discussing this with *you*. It's time for my cocoa and bed."

"Can you at least help me out of here, please?" asked Lennie.

The Earl looked down his very long nose in disgust.

"I wouldn't dirty my paws for the likes of you!"

"Please can you tell Badger where I am then? He'll help me out."

"If I must," sneered the Earl.

Lennie's head slumped as the Earl strolled off in the direction of Badger's garden.

Badger was busy pinning more feathers to the basketball ring when the Earl arrived to tell him of Lennie's whereabouts.

Badger sped to the sandpit and saw only Lennie's eyes and ears peeking out, looking very distressed.

"Just sit tight, Lennie. I'll get you out of this."

"I've been sitting tight for ages" spluttered Lennie.

"This calls for a bit of assistance" said Badger. He tapped his trusty neckerchief and closed his eyes.

"Okay 'Chief, Show koo ray, show koo ray, Help me shovel this sand away!"

Sparkles of light appeared, as 'Chief unravelled, swirled around, flattened out and stiffened. It shot towards Lennie and began to dig. Badger jumped into the sandpit and dug frantically, too.

Lennie's chest emerged, and as the sand started to pull away further, he was able to free his paws and ease himself out slowly. 'Chief flew back to Badger's neck.

"Badger, thank you, thank you. I had another nightmare. It was horrible. I don't know whether this was part of the dream of not, but I met the Earl, and he let it slip that his development plans are for right here, in the lane!"

Badger stopped suddenly. "He said *what*?"

"It might have been part of my nightmare Badger, I don't know. But I think he plans to do it *here*."

"I think it was real enough. It was the Earl who told me you were in the sandpit, after all."

"And he wants all of us out!" cried Lennie.

Badger shook his head. "I've seen this before with him, Lennie. He is ruthless. He has no mercy, and no understanding of what makes a community, such as ours, in the lane. We have to stop him. Immediately!"

Chapter Five

The next day, Badger and Lennie were sharing some much needed toast.

"I can't believe he didn't tell me," said Badger. "He's staying here with me. He showed me his plans, but I had no idea it was on my patch. This is serious."

Lennie nodded.

Badger peered through the crack in the fence and looked fondly out into the lane.

"Look at the alley cats with their wonderful Meowzik Maker. Do you remember how they helped with the *Barking Boogie*? Hamish and Lucky live only a few gardens up. And at the far end is PLOPP, the drop-in centre, Timmy and Snif's creation; an amazing place. You live there, Lennie. Even Pogo Paws and Pickle, as much as they annoy you; that's where their home is too.

But most of all there's the wise old oak tree, scene of so many adventures and our best server of p-mails," said Badger.

"I know," sighed Lennie sadly.

Badger squinted up at the hot sun high in the sky.

"The Earl should be here anytime. It's time for his lunch. Now Lennie, to other matters. We need to get these nightmares of yours sorted. Did the milk and cinnamon help at all?"

"Oh no!" remembered Lennie. "The jam jars must have got buried in the sand."

"Never mind. We need to find out what's really causing your nightmares, and I know the very thing to help with that."

Badger checked his sundial. He looked to see where the shadow was. "Nearly there. The Wim-Wim will be here shortly and then we can take flight."

"Take flight? But I can't fly," worried Lennie.

"Don't worry, we'll sort that out too," reassured Badger.

Just then, a long nose appeared through the crack in the fence, followed by the Earl of Doodlepoppington's elegant form.

"Good day, chaps. Ah, Lennie, I see you made it safely out of that ghastly sandpit," he said.

Badger bristled, but tried to remain calm.

"When were you going to tell me, cousin?" he asked through gritted teeth.

"Tell you what?" said the Earl, shifting uneasily from paw to paw.

"About your plans for the lane, of course," said Badger.

"Oh, *that*. Isn't it marvellous?" The Earl nodded to Lennie. "Your friends, Pogo Paws and Pickle, are proving to be quite an asset on that front."

"You mean you've tricked them into helping you somehow?" said Badger.

"Where did you get that idea from?" asked the Earl.

"Erm ... *everything* you've *ever* been involved with. It's the way you work," said Badger.

"Now, listen here," said the Earl coldly. "This will be great for the lane. It's about time we got rid of all those waifs and strays, and clutter and jumble, and took the place upmarket. No cousin of mine should be living in such a hovel."

Badger's dander was ruffled.

"But *here* is my home; *these* are my friends; and *this* is our community. You have no right to destroy it!"

Just then Badger heard the familiar clang and clatter of the Wim-Wim's arrival.

"I have to go now," said Badger. "But I warn you

49

Doodles, if you set one paw in the lane whilst I'm away, there will be trouble.

The Earl stood to attention and saluted him.

"Whatever you say, Badger, whatever you say," said the Earl with a chuckle.

Badger took Lennie by the paw and led him to the Wim-Wim. Lennie hesitated.

"What's *that*?" He pointed.

"It's the Wim-Wim for a wowser to wind the weather up on a wet day, of course," said Badger.

"Blimey!" said Lennie.

"Why don't you come in and take a seat?" invited Badger.

"Is *this* the famous flying machine?" asked Lennie.

"Yes, the Wim-Wim *can* fly," said Badger, "but we're not flying anywhere right now. Just come in and relax."

As Lennie sat down gingerly in the Wim-Wim, Badger tapped his neckerchief quietly. It slowly unravelled from his neck and hung like a medallion. It swung gently from side to side in front of Lennie's eyes with a heavy knot at the bottom.

"Look at that!" said Badger. "Now, focus on the knot."

Lennie's eyes followed the rhythm of the swaying knot back and forth, to and fro, until his eyelids drooped.

Badger closed his eyes and whispered:
"*Into the Land of Nod we go,*
Where all is good and dreams can grow,
High and free in Cuckoo Land,
Where clouds will give us a helping hand."
Very quickly, Lennie was in a deep contented sleep.

Badger turned the golden key on the side of the Wim-Wim and soon they were high in the midday sky, on their way to the Crystal Cave to put a stop to Lennie's nightmares.

But while all was peaceful inside the Wim-Wim, if Badger had zoomed down into the lane beneath him at that moment, he would have seen a sight that would have made him gasp in horror.

The Earl had brought in his Digger Dogs ... and they were digging up the lane.

Chapter Six

"Woohooooooooooooooooooooooooo!" yelled Badger.

"What, what? Where are we?" shouted Lennie, jumping awake with the noise.

"We're in the Wim-Wim, and we're on our way to the Crystal Cave," said Badger.

"Flying? Me? Surely not? I'm scared of flying," said Lennie.

"Not any more, my friend. Now, hold on tight and help me. I'm trying to find Nippy Nimbus."

"Nippy who?"

"He's just a cloud, but he's generally grumpy. He's the gatekeeper to the Enchanted Forest."

"Grumpy clouds? Enchanted forests? Am I dreaming again?" asked Lennie.

Aha, there he is!" Badger pulled a lever on the Wim-Wim and it shot upwards at speed.

The Wim-Wim hurtled right into the middle of the cloud and landed with a bump.

"Hello, Nippy. Long time, no see," said Badger.

The cloud groaned. "Still too soon. Give me the password, Mutt, and you can be on your way."

"Now, let me think, could it be 'California Dreaming?'" He turned to Lennie and said: "I remember that so vividly from my days in Hollywood, sunbathing on Venice Beach."

"Nope!" said Nippy gleefully. "Just two more tries."

"Okay. How about 'All I have to do is dream, dream, dream ...?'"

"Too obvious, Badger. Try again."

"Aha! Well, it's got to be 'Daydream Believer', surely?"

"You've done it again Badger, on your way" grumbled Nippy.

A misty trapdoor opened in front of them. They jumped out of the Wim-Wim and peered through the fog.

"This isn't the usual way in, Nippy," frowned Badger.

"Well, I thought you'd like a bit of a bounce this time," the cloud chuckled, "just to keep it interesting."

"Hold my paw, Lennie, and follow me," yelled Badger as they both leapt forward into the void.

Boing, boing boing! With cloud after cloud cushioning their fall, they arrived with an abrupt thump on a spiky, black shrubbery. Nearby they could see glaring, flashing neon lights.

Lennie rubbed his eyes.

"Ow!" he said, rubbing his bottom. "Where *are* we, Badger?"

Badger scratched his head and rubbed his bottom too. "I'm really not very sure, Lennie, but I'm sure Nippy thinks he's hilarious. Hang on, there's a sign."

To their left, near the flashing lights, was a big placard with the words:

YOU ARE NOT VERY WELCOME TO THE BACK OF BEYOND,

WHERE ALL YOUR FEARS RESIDE.

TAKE YOUR SEATS ON THE DREAM DODGEMS.

SIT BACK, AND ENJOY THE RIDE."

"Are we at a fun fair?" asked Lennie. "Because it's a bit dark."

"Uh oh!" said Badger. "This wasn't *quite* what I had in mind."

Badger and Lennie walked up to the waiting dodgem and climbed inside.

"Deep breaths. Lennie. We can do this. It's the only way we can get beyond the Back of Beyond," said Badger, smiling weakly.

Lennie, who was now speechless, clung on to the steering wheel.

The dodgem moved off at alarming speed. All around them, other bumper cars whirled and whizzed past. A thumping disco beat thudded in their ears, and the walls were daubed with colourful graffiti. Suddenly, through the flicker and flash of the light, one of the dodgems veered towards them. It was filled with a shoal of wibbly-wobbly jellyfish.

"Swerve, Lennie, quick," shouted Badger, grabbing the wheel, as another car filled with scorpions and snakes jolted them from behind.

"Ow!" yelped Lennie. He spun the car around quickly, and booted the dodgem face-on. A flare of light sparked and the car dissolved into thin air.

With their knuckles frozen to the
steering wheel, they whirled and birled
at great speed as rubber banged against
rubber. A dodgem hit them sharply from the
right. Badger and Lennie jerked. Pogo Paws
and Pickle were at the wheel of the other
car.

"C'mon, Lennie. Hit the pedal, give it
some wellie!" yelled Badger.

Lennie stamped his paw
on the pedal, and the dodgem
swirled round to face them. He
rammed them hard.

"You two don't
scare me. See
you!" And with that,
another explosion
of light, and the
dodgem vanished.

Just as they were
breathing a
sigh of relief, a
car ambushed
them from
the left, filled with
two mountain-sized
mallets and fifty watering cans.

"Take that!" shouted Lennie, as he
bumped its bumper into oblivion. *Woooooosh!*
Another spark and the car evaporated.

Lennie yanked the wheel and whirled the
dodgem round. Badger held on to the pole
in amazement at his friend's new-found

confidence. Facing them now was a camel in a car, with fifteen quivering humps.

"Hold on!" said Lennie to Badger. "This could be bumpy." Lennie thrust the car towards the camel and bumped the humps, one after another. As he hit the last hump, the car combusted and faded into the ether.

All of a sudden, everything was quiet and dark. Then, they heard an ominous judder. The lights came on, and in front of them was Badger's worst nightmare: a Snaffletuck; the legendary toast-rustling beast. Its head was wide, and its mouth was oblong with gnashing fangs. It drove a juggernaut dodgem with digger jaws of steel.

Badger grabbed the wheel.

"This one's mine!" he said, pushing his paw down full-throttle on the pedal.

"You may take my Buddy Bites, but you will *never* take my toast!" shouted Badger, smashing his dodgem into the oncoming monstrosity. But his opponent didn't flinch. The Snaffletuck simply slobbered, then reversed and revved his giant dodgem again.

"Uh oh!" blustered Badger. "Time for a spell!" He closed his eyes and quickly yelled the magic words.

"*Make that dodgem slip and skid,*
With butter, oil and ink of squid.
Save the toast from being snaffled,
And make the monster totally baffled."

62

The Snaffletuck's dodgem started to spin, twirling around and around at speed before disappearing in a puff of smoke.

All was quiet. The one remaining light bulb flickered. The track was empty but for Badger and Lennie's dodgem car.

Ding Ding! Ding Ding! Two tickets popped up on the dashboard. Badger leaned forward and studied them.

"Well done, Dodgem Dodgers. You've faced your fears head-on, and you've beaten them. Now, you've arrived at the Front of Beyond. Enjoy your journey onwards."

Badger and Lennie fell out of the car grasping their tickets.

"What a trip!" said Badger, catching his breath.

"That was epic!" gasped Lennie.

"All the fun of the fair, Lennie. Now, come on. We've got things to do and things to see. Follow me."

Badger made his way through the undergrowth and back onto the golden-leaved path he knew and loved.

"This is more like it," said Lennie.

"And now, I have someone very special I'd like you to meet." Badger whistled and his friend, Baby Unicorn, emerged out of the trees.

Lennie froze.

"That's a unicorn! An actual unicorn!" he whispered.

"Yes, Lennie, and he's come to help us cure your nightmares."

Lennie bowed his head as the unicorn approached. He hung behind Badger and kept his head low.

"Hi, Badger. Heard you had a bumpy ride on the way in today."

"Yes, that was Nippy's idea of a prank, but we made it okay."

"So, who's your friend? And how can I help?"

"This is Lennie, and he's having terrible trouble with nightmares. He's also the leader of the gang."

"Okay, follow me," said Baby Unicorn.

Badger and Lennie followed the beautiful

and the Daydream Drivers

creature along the golden-leaved path. They passed signs for "Nearly There" and "There", and soon after arrived at the mouth of the Crystal Cave.

It dazzled and sparkled.

Lennie fainted.

Chapter Seven

When Lennie opened his eyes, he saw a huge horn and two big eyes peering down at him.

"Hello, Lennie," winked Baby Unicorn. "Welcome to the Crystal Cave."

"This is the best dream ever!" yelled Lennie.

"Except it's not a dream," said Badger helping him to his feet.

Lennie looked around, wide-eyed. He was surrounded by thousands of glittering luminous crystals.

"I'm in the Crystal Cave," he whispered. "I'm actually *in* the Crystal Cave."

"You'd better believe it," smiled Badger. "Come on. Baby Unicorn has something to show us."

Lennie and Badger followed the unicorn through the cave, stepping over crystal rocks pulsating with light, through shimmering archways and walls of sparkle, until they reached an open nook at the back.

"Now, let's see what we can discover about what's been giving you these dreadful nightmares Lennie," said Badger comfortingly.

Baby Unicorn pointed his horn towards the cave wall. Suddenly, it lit up and flickered into action, like a movie screen. There, Badger and Lennie saw two young dogs in a boxing ring. Lots of Big Folk were jeering and cheering around the edges. One of the dogs had his snout taped up, and was pestering and annoying the other. The other dog was baring its teeth and snarling viciously.

Lennie pointed at the smaller dog on the screen: "That looks like me, Badger."

"I think it *is* you, Lennie. That tape must have really hurt your nose," he said.

Lennie rubbed his nose and winced. He was starting to remember the awful time before he arrived in the lane. He looked up at the screen again. It showed the two dogs being led away from the boxing ring. Lennie was taken to a big cage where his brother, Louie, was kept.

"How did it go, Lennie?" asked his brother.

"It was a nightmare, but I did my job. The other dog is really angry now, and ready for a fight. He's the most feared street fighter in the world, Louie. I wish you didn't have to fight him, and I wish I could help you escape," said Lennie, whimpering.

"There's nothing I can do, Lennie. I've just got to get in there and hope for the best," sighed his brother.

Lennie watched as the Big Folk opened the cage and led his brother out into the pit. He closed his eyes and covered his head, but no matter how hard he tried, he could not shut out the sound of the growls, the yowls, the howls, the screeches and the snarls coming from the vicious brawl.

Back in the cave, Lennie sobbed.

"It was the last time I ever saw him. I couldn't bear to see him all battered. I ran away when the Big Folk weren't looking, and that's how I ended up on the lane. I remember it all now."

"Do you know whether your brother made it?" asked Badger gently.

"I don't see how he could have. That other dog was a prizefighter, and they fight until the end... until there is only one dog standing. I was lucky. I was just a bait dog." Lennie shook his head sadly.

"Is that why you don't want to lead the gang? Because of the fighting?" asked Badger.

"Yes. The Big Folk handlers forced me to rankle my brother's opponents, so that they would fight harder. And now, Pogo Paws and Pickle are always on at me to be nastier, and to act like their leader. But it's just not who I am!" Lennie whispered.

Badger looked kindly at his friend, and said: "No, I don't think that's who you are either. Okay, I think we need to help you relax and then maybe the nightmares will go. Fancy a trip to the Zen Den?"

Lennie brightened. "It can't be any worse than the Back of Beyond, can it?"

Badger smiled "No, it's a completely different place. Anyway, you bumped those fears away good and proper, didn't you?"

As Lennie and Badger turned to go, the light flickered again on the screen.

"Ahem, not just yet, boys. There's more to see," said Baby Unicorn, tapping his horn on the ground.

They looked back at the screen to see The Earl of Doodlepoppington as a pup looking up to an older dog. He was being lectured sternly by his father, the Duke.

"Now listen here, boy. In order to succeed like I have, you must throw out all these notions of compassion and care, and step over anyone who gets in your way."

"But it makes me feel good to share my toys with the local dogs" pleaded the Earl.

"Nonsense! You're so much better than those mangy mutts. You should do as I do, and boot them out of the way. Like this!" The older dog kicked his son squarely on the chin. The Earl yelped and rolled over.

Badger and Lennie watched as the Earl got to his feet, hung his head, and said, "Yes, of course, father, I will do as you say."

As the screen faded, Badger turned to Lennie wisely, and said, "Now, at last, we know why the Earl acts the way he does."

Badger bowed towards the unicorn and said:"As ever, thank you, Baby Unicorn. This has let us understand everything so much better."

"Enjoy the Zen Den. I've left you a little surprise," winked Baby Unicorn.

Badger and Lennie left the cave and set off on the golden-leaved path once more.

Badger sniffed the air and caught the gentle aroma of geranium.

"I think it's this way, Lennie," he shouted, as he veered off to the left.

"What's that?" yelled Lennie, pointing over at a signpost, which said, 'Fill with the Chill'.

"Looks like we're getting closer," said Badger, spotting another sign further along, which said, 'Go with the Flow'.

Lennie heard a faint tinkle in the trees. He looked up to see silver wind chimes fluttering in the breeze.

Badger sniffed the scent of patchouli and breathed in deeply. Lennie took a deep breath too. Up ahead, they saw fairy lights twinkling.

"There it is," said Badger, passing yet a nother sign saying, 'Relax to the Max'.

74

The path was strewn with sweet-smelling petals, which tickled their paws, and led up to a wooden cabin. A million fireflies shimmered all around them.

They stepped up onto the veranda and saw a sign saying: 'WELCOME TO THE ZEN DEN. LEAVE YOUR DOUBTS AT THE DOOR, AND REMOVE ALL GLOOMINESS BEFORE ENTERING'.

The door glided effortlessly open and
a waft of lavender filled the air. A soft
melody floated past their ears. The floor was
covered with sumptuous velvet cushions.

"Wow!" said Lennie, looking around the
room. "This is amazing!" Then he saw it,
dangling in the window; a perfectly formed
Dreamcatcher with a tag attached. It had

feathers of different shapes and sizes, and all the colours of the rainbow. It shone with jewels.

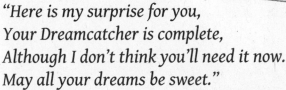

"The jewels of Jupiter!" smiled Badger. He read out Baby Unicorn's message;

"Here is my surprise for you,
Your Dreamcatcher is complete,
Although I don't think you'll need it now.
May all your dreams be sweet."

"Now, are you ready to relax, Lennie? Choose a cushion and make yourself comfortable." Badger sat down with his back legs crossed, and held out his front paws. Lennie did the same.

Badger took a deep breath and said: "Close your eyes, Lennie, and take a deep, deep breath. In ... and out. In ... and out. Empty your head of all your worries about Pogo Paws and Pickle, and just sit in this moment of absolute calm," he whispered. "Now, begin to believe in yourself, picture good things ahead, and soon, all your days will be badgical magical."

They both sat breathing in the beautiful smells, feeling very contented.

"When you're ready, Lennie," whispered Badger, "wiggle your paws and open your eyes. There! How does that feel?"

"I feel like I'm floating," replied a very relaxed Lennie.

Just then, a cuckoo clock chimed.

"That's our cue to go." Badger jumped up.

As they made their way to the door, the cuckoo flew off the clock and onto a wooden box. The bird tapped its beak on the lid which opened to reveal a parcel wrapped in ribbon with a tag that said: 'Life is full of surprises, and here's one just for you'.

Badger untied the ribbon carefully to find four buttery slices of toast for the journey home from Baby Unicorn.

"The Zen Den is my most favourite place ever," smiled Badger, tying the ribbon around Lennie's head like a bandanna, and grabbing the Dreamcatcher.

As they stepped outside the cabin, Badger heard the familiar rattle and hum of the Wim-Wim.

"How do you feel about our journey home now, Lennie? Ready to soar into the stars?" asked Badger.

Lennie smiled blissfully. "I'm super-chilled, and ready for anything," he replied.

Badger chuckled and climbed into the Wim-Wim, followed by an extremely laid-back Lennie.

They flew back to Badger's garden.

As they tumbled out of the Wim-Wim, they heard a loud commotion and the whirring of a chainsaw.

They peered out into the lane where to their horror; the old oak tree was tied up in chains. A team of fierce looking Digger Dogs in hard hats and high-vis jackets surrounded the faithful tree. The Earl was at the centre brandishing a gleaming chainsaw.

Badger and Lennie scrambled through the crack in the fence and sped towards the crowd screaming "Stopppppppppppppppppppppppppppppppppppppppppp!"

But it looked like they were already too late.

Chapter Eight

When the assembled crowd turned round, they could only see Lennie. Badger was already flying high above the old oak tree. The Earl tutted, and turned back to his chainsaw. He pulled the cord, ready to slice into the tree. Badger tapped 'Chief urgently, and said: *'Turn at once with utmost zeal, into a shield of solid steel'.*

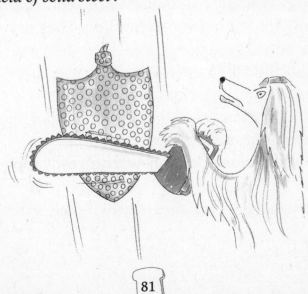

'Chief shot downwards and slid between the bark of the old oak tree and the jaws of the menacing blade. Sparks flew as steel slammed into steel, and the Earl leapt backwards in shock. He looked up to see Badger plummeting towards him. The Mystical Mutt landed squarely with a thump on top of the Earl, and flattened him to the ground.

"Stay there, 'Chief!" ordered Badger. "You did well. You've saved the tree."

"For now, but I'll be back," warned the Earl, dusting himself down. "This lane is mine now, Badger. And don't you forget it. It's only home to a motley bunch of scruffs and strays. They mean nothing. They drag the whole area down. This lane will be beautiful when I'm finished with it; very des-res for high-class pooches."

"Don't you care at all about the community that has been built up here? This is where dogs and cats get on. Timmy and Snif set up PLOPP, the drop-in centre at the end of the lane; it's where we've had amazing times with *Pet Idol* and the *Barking Boogie.* It's where we all look out for each other. And you want to stamp on all that?"

"That's all very touching, I'm sure," scoffed the Earl, as he threw down a pile of papers. "Just make sure everyone gets one of these." And off he strode.

Badger and Lennie looked at the papers. At the top of each page, in large writing, it said: 'Eviction Order'. Pogo Paws and Pickle drew close, the alley cats drew closer, the birds fluttered in a flurry above, and all the other strays from the lane gasped.

"It says everyone has to be out by sundown tomorrow," said Lennie.

"Good luck finding new homes. We've already got one!" boasted Pickle.

"Yes!" added Pogo Paws proudly. "The Earl's promised us one of his new-builds."

"Oh really?" said Badger raising an eyebrow. "I wouldn't be so sure. Did he stamp his paw on any paperwork for you?"

Pogo Paws and Pickle looked at each other and shook their heads.

"If I were you, I'd be checking that new house contract as soon as possible," said Badger.

Pogo Paws and Pickle sped off in a panic to confront the Earl. Badger looked sadly at the devastation of the lane.

Earth was piled high, underground pipes lay exposed, planks of wood were stacked against the fence, and the sandpit had been completely dug up. The wheelie bins lay open on their sides.

The lane was almost unrecognisable.

"We have to stop this" said Badger. "Everyone here is losing their homes through no fault of their own. If we don't do something, it will never be the same again. What right does he have to destroy this community? I'm ashamed to admit he's a relative of mine."

The assembled crowd muttered their agreement.

"We could find another lane, but it wouldn't be the same," said the leader of the alley cats.

"The lane has the best worms in the country," sang the birds, harmoniously.

"I feel safe here, even though I've got to live alongside Pogo Paws and Pickle," said Lennie.

"We need to think of a plan, and fast," said Badger.

Just then, Lennie spotted something familiar peeking out of a pile of rubble. He tapped Badger on the shoulder and pointed. There was a perfectly intact jam jar with a hopping mad flea inside.

"Of course!" said Badger joyfully. "We'll send him packing with a flea in his ear. It's time to open that jam jar!"

Chapter Nine

Badger carefully twisted the lid of the jam jar loose and whispered: *"Remember now to jump and bounce, to make the Earl flinch and flounce."* He chuckled to himself.

The flea wobbled slightly as it crawled out of the jar, and then hopped along the lane to find the Earl of Doodlepoppington.

Pogo Paws and Pickle had already found him.

"So?" demanded Pogo Paws "When can we move in to our new luxury doghouse, boss?"

"What *are* you talking about?" snapped the Earl.

"The brand new home you promised us?" added Pickle.

The Earl tutted. "Now, why on earth would I just hand over one of my pet palaces to the likes of you two ruffians? I'm trying to improve the neighbourhood, not drag it down even further."

"But you promised us; in return for recruiting the Digger Dogs for digging, the Sniffer Dogs for finding the pipes, and the Security Dogs for safety," whined Pogo Paws.

"I'm afraid, I really can't recall. Do you have a contract? Show me where I've put my paw-print, and I'll gladly honour the deal."

Pogo Paws and Pickle looked at each other blankly.

"No? Haven't got one? I thought as much. Now run along. I expect you

have some packing to do. You have to leave the lane by sundown tomorrow," said the Earl firmly.

Pogo Paws looked at Pickle in panic, as she fumed silently.

"You won't get away with this!" she snarled.

"Whatever!" smirked the Earl, and swept off down the lane.

"Now what are we to do?" asked Pogo Paws. "We've got nowhere to go and we've turned our back on our pals in the lane."

"We've been conned good and proper," said Pickle angrily. "Right, we need to go and see Badger. The Earl is his cousin, after all. Badger got us into this mess. He can get us out. So, let's look like we're truly sorry, and Badger will help us. Perhaps, together, we can oust that scoundrel once and for all from our patch."

"We'll have to be quick then. He wants us out by tomorrow," puffed Pogo Paws, as he ran to catch up with a determined Pickle.

Back in Badger's garden, Lennie was

enjoying a nap in the afternoon sunshine, while Badger busied himself with a new task. Happily, he hummed as he hammered nails into wooden poles and mounted big white cards. He was making an assortment of placards. He rooted in his plant pot to find a paintbrush and bright paint.

Throughout the noise, Lennie slept soundly. For once, he was having a pleasant dream. In his slumbers, he was running towards a figure in the distance. As he drew closer, he could see that it was his long-lost brother, Louie. Lennie hugged him.

"I need to tell you something really important about the Earl. You must stand up to him, and for what you believe in. You've got friends. He doesn't. There's a real strength in friendship, so use it well," said his brother gently.

Before Lennie could reply, his brother turned and ran off again into the distance.

Lennie tried to follow him but his legs wouldn't move. He looked down and

saw that they had turned to strawberry blancmange.

When he woke up, he was licking his legs. He was sure they tasted sugary.

He looked over to see Badger sewing his red-spotted neckerchief. It was a little frayed from its job as a shield against the chainsaw.

"You're awake at last. No nightmares today?" asked Badger. He tied his mended neckerchief back around his neck and tapped it gratefully.

"I had a lovely dream about my brother, who was giving me some good advice," smiled Lennie.

"Then you should heed it. Dreams have a funny way of helping us see problems clearly."

Hmmm, thought Lennie, *perhaps I will.*

"Look at what I've been doing," said Badger proudly, displaying his artwork.

In front of him, leaning against the fence were a number of placards with painted slogans.

One read "LOLA: Leave our Lane alone!"

Another said: "Let sleeping dogs lie!"

Another: "You are barking up the wrong tree!"

Lennie pointed at one of them "What does P-O-O-L mean?"

"Oops! Forgot that one." Badger daubed some more paint on the sign, which now read: "Paws off our Lane!"

"This one's my favourite though." He giggled and nodded to a larger sign.

It read: "You put the 'doo doo' in doodle!"

"Gosh, you've been busy. What are they all for?" said Lennie admiringly.

"I propose that we stage a peaceful protest against the lane development," said Badger.

"Count me in. We've got to stand up to bullies like the Earl," said Lennie bravely.

"I've sent p-mails to the surrounding neighbourhoods as well, because this has an impact beyond our lane. I'm sure he won't just stop here," said Badger.

"We could start a p-mail petition too," suggested Lennie.

"Good thinking. Now, I've asked that we all gather at the old oak tree in an hour. Then we can march to the other end of the lane, and show the Earl just how much we're all against his plans," said Badger.

"That is, if he's not already scarpered in horror at having a flea," laughed Lennie.

The flea had carried out its task and had lodged itself in the Earl's rump. He started

to scratch. His graceful body was prickling with a burning, and most unbecoming itch. He delved deep into his long coat and pulled out a garlic bulb.

This should do the trick, he thought, as he set to work peeling the bulb, and rubbing the cloves all over his skin.

Very quickly, the irritating itch stopped. He smiled to himself and thought: *Another point in my favour. If I can show this lane to have a flea infestation from the mucky grubsters living here, then everyone will back my plans.*

Further down the lane, Pogo Paws and Pickle crept through the crack in the fence into Badger's garden with their tails low.

"Ahem!" said Pogo Paws meekly.

Badger and Lennie turned from the placards to see two sorry figures standing, with their heads hung respectfully.

"We've come to help you stop the Earl and his plans," said Pickle.

"Help us?" asked Lennie in surprise. "But I thought you were on the Earl's side, and he was giving you one of the luxury dog houses?"

"Erm, not quite," said Pogo Paws sheepishly.

"We've decided we don't like his plans, and anyway, technically, as you, Lennie, are still our leader, then we should be taking orders from you," said Pickle endearingly.

Lennie, who was speechless, looked at them both suspiciously.

"Okay," said Badger quickly. "Well, better late than never. Grab some of these signs, and let's head to the oak tree to meet the others.

There was a tremendous crowd gathered when they arrived at the tree. Word had spread far and wide across the surrounding areas. Some had brought shiny bin lids as shields, others had their own placards. Even the birds had tied bells and ribbons to their tiny feet.

Badger climbed on top of a wooden crate, held up a megaphone and addressed the crowd.

"I see before me a whole bunch of my friends, who are opposed to this development. You have come to protest peacefully as free dogs and cats, and free dogs and cats you will stay. We have one chance to tell the Earl that he may try to take our community, but he will *never* take our freedom!"

The crowd cheered, jubilant to join

forces, and be part of the protest march
with the Mystical Mutt at the helm.

Badger yelled "Where do we live?"
The crowd shouted back to him "In the
lane!"

"Where do we meet?" continued Badger.

"In the lane!" they chanted back.

"And what do we love?"

"We love the lane!"

"Okay, let's go then," said Badger leading the crowd onwards.

They all strode up the lane with their heads held high, their hearts filled with passion and roused into action.

Strutting towards them was the defiant Earl, flanked by his squad of ferocious Security Dogs. The two opposing sides met in the middle. Badger stepped forward first and the Earl stepped forward, until the two dogs were almost nose to nose. The two cousins looked each other squarely in the eyes.

"Yuk!" shouted Badger, stepping backwards

The crowd gasped. Surely Badger wasn't giving in already?

"What's that smell?" he winced.

"That, my dear boy, is the delicate aroma of garlic cloves. I'm afraid I had an

99

unfortunate encounter with an annoying flea earlier, and as I'm sure you know, fleas are no fans of garlic."

"Oh!" said Badger grimacing, as he realised that his flea plan had been foiled.

"It does, however, highlight one more reason to clean up this lane and put in some quality housing. It will attract a better, cleaner breed of dog and cat. So, unless you want me to call in the Pong Police to deal with the fleas (and you know that their poison is *not* mutt-friendly), I suggest you and your crew back off now, and simply accept that I, as usual, have won," the Earl boasted.

As Badger thought of a reply, he heard a tiny voice and felt a twitch on his snout. He crossed his eyes to focus.

"Hello. Yes, it's me, little old flea. Count me in!" said the little creature on the end of his nose. Suddenly there was an almighty roar as the Security Dogs shouted "Charge!"

They barked, they growled, they snarled, they spat and bared their vicious fangs.

As the fierce dogs leapt into action and pounced on Badger's peaceful protest, the Earl slipped quietly away.

Pogo Paws and Pickle caught several Security Dogs with their bin lids, and clanged their heads together like cymbals. The birds swooped down and tied their

enemy's paws up with ribbon. Badger
pointed his ears forward to the heap of
discarded sand and commanded: "*Wind now
whistle into a gust, and turn this lane to a fog of
dust.*"

The sand whirled into the air and soon,
everyone was rubbing their eyes.

But as both sides started to retreat,
Lennie was still in the thick of it. He was
caught between the jaws of a three-legged,
one-eyed monster. The dog threw him
against the fence and just as he was about to
lunge for Lennie, he froze.

Chapter Ten

Lennie's long-lost brother Louie stood before him.

"Lennie, is that you?"

"Is that really you, Louie? Am I dreaming again?" cried Lennie.

"It's really me, Lennie, and no you're definitely *not* dreaming. Let me get you out of here, it's too dangerous. Quick, follow me."

Louie led Lennie towards the pond, where all was quiet apart from the ducks.

"What happened to you after I fled that day?" Lennie asked anxiously.

"Well as you can see, I lost a leg in the fight, but I adapted quickly. I'm known as Tri-pawed now." Louie laughed. "And I got a nasty gash on my eye, so in the end it just closed up. I think my eyeball's still in there."

"But how did you manage to get away from the Big Folk handlers?"

"They left me for dead, Lennie, and I played dead until I was sure they had gone. I managed to get to a main road, and then the heavens smiled upon me. A local Big Folk vet was passing and picked me up. I'll never forget the kindness he showed me."

"But I don't understand. How did you end up here, working for the Earl?"

"Well, the Big Folk vet operated and looked after me for a while, but he couldn't keep me for ever. He took me to the pound. I stayed there for weeks, but I wasn't exactly a good-looking pet for a new Big Folk family." Louie smiled weakly. "So, I made my escape. I heard the Earl was hiring ferocious guard dogs, so I got the job."

"Oh no. But that means we're on different sides, Louie".

"I don't know the reason for the quarrel, Lennie. I'm just a tail for hire. But I know this; I'm tired and fed up with fighting".

"Then, please, will you help us, Louie? And then let me look after you. I've spent so long missing you. You can retire, and I can make sure you get food and water. You'll have family and friendship. What could be better than that?"

Louie looked doubtfully at Lennie.

"But I'm your big brother. *I* should be looking after *you*."

"Just you being here with me will be all the looking after I need. Please say yes?" pleaded Lennie.

"Okay!" said Louie brightly. "Tell me what needs to be done."

Back in the lane, the dust had settled and all was quiet. The Earl crept back to the battle scene. All of the protestors had vanished; all except Badger.

"So, this is what it's come to Doodles, is it?" said Badger sadly.

"Well, what do you expect? I've never lost before. I don't see why I should start now," said the Earl coldly.

"You've never lost before? That's not entirely true though is it?" said Badger.

"I have *no* idea what you're talking about."

"Well, you lost out on the chance to get to spend time with your mother. Didn't your father the Duke, meet her on a trip to Persia? Wasn't she part Afghan, part Saluki, and most definitely *not* a pure-breed like the Doodlepoppington clan? And then she went home to her own family, when she'd had enough of his blusters and blunders."

"My father said she didn't want me," said the Earl forlornly.

"Not true! She tried to take you with her, but he wouldn't allow it."

"Are you in contact with her?" asked the Earl.

"Now and again" said Badger softly "We keep in touch with the odd p-mail, and she always asks how you are getting on. I'll be sorry to tell her of your latest exploits, of course."

As the Earl turned to leave, looking a little less commanding than he had earlier, two of his Security Dogs rushed up to him breathless.

"It's the Duke of Doodlepoppington, Sir. We've just picked up an urgent p-mail for you."

Both Badger and the Earl stood still and waited to hear the news from Upper Barkingford.

"He's run off with the little poodle that gives away free samples from the doggy chocs factory," said the smaller of the dogs.

"Hah!" scoffed the Earl "That's not news! He's always had a sweet tooth!"

"But that's not all, Sir," said the larger of the dogs. "The p-mail also said that he's sold up everything, including your home!"

Chapter Eleven

As eviction day dawned, news had quickly spread of the Earl's loss of his own home.

Badger had made his cousin, who was in shock, comfortable in his shed, with his best blankets and most buttery of toast.

"I'm sorry for what's happened, Doodles," said Badger apologetically. "I know that Upper Barkingford is where you grew up, and is the only place you've ever called home. You can stay on here as long as you want, of course."

The Earl harrumphed. "My father is a brute to do this. But in a funny sort of way, I feel free. He was forever telling me I was doing things wrong. And I can't believe that my mother wanted to see me and he never told me."

"I suppose we should let her know what's happened. Maybe you could send her a p-mail?" suggested Badger.

"I'd like that very much. I was really small when she left. I can't even remember her face."

"Maybe not, but we dogs never forget a smell." Badger smiled.

"Indeed! However, in the meantime, without the stately pile in Upper Barkingford, I have no home and no funds." He frowned.

"What does this mean for your plans for the lane?" asked Badger hopefully.

"I'm afraid, they must go ahead. Without my income from the home estate, I have to actually earn something now. The lane seems like the best option, as work has already begun. So the eviction orders still stand."

Badger groaned.

Out in the lane, Louie was rallying the troops. The Sniffer, Digger and Security Dogs had all downed tools and were gathered around their three-legged, one-eyed colleague.

"Are you all aware that the boss has no funds now to pay us for our work?"

The crowd of dogs griped and grumbled restlessly.

"This is unfair treatment when we've all worked so hard," added Louie, stirring up the bunch even more. "So will you join me in a walkout?"

The throng surged forward with cheers.

As the crowd dispersed, Lennie, who had been watching from the side, shouted, "Well done!" to his brother. Louie hopped off the makeshift scaffolding to meet him.

"That should do it" he said cheerfully "Let's see how the Earl manages when he has to get his *own* paws dirty."

"All the same, I do feel a little sorry for him. He *has* just lost his home," said Lennie sadly.

Badger and the Earl were returning to his shed, after sending a p-mail to the Earl's mother, when they bumped into the alley cats.

"We are sorry for your loss, Mister Doodlepops, and we bring you this fish for supper."

"Erm, thank you most kindly," said the Earl uncomfortably.

As they rounded the corner, Pogo Paws and Pickle ran up to them with a fresh chop from the butcher's yard.

"This wasn't my idea," said Pickle

reluctantly. "Pogo Paws here thought we should offer our sympathies, and that this chop might cheer you up. We're still annoyed with you."

"Thank you very much," replied the Earl drooling at the sight of the chop.

As they reached Badger's garden, Lennie appeared with a bag of Crunchy Munchy Chewy Chops.

"I thought you might like some of these,"
said Lennie.

"Thank you. Now come and join me,
dear fellow. Perhaps we can all share them
together?"

Badger, Lennie and the Earl slipped through the crack in the fence and lay down on the grass.

"I don't understand it," said the Earl. "Surely, I'm enemy number one around here? Yet everyone is being so kind."

"That's what community is all about, Doodles. Sometimes we can put our differences aside for the greater good. You've just had a shock, and despite what you think, you've been around here long enough now for our friends to care about you. That's what you'll be destroying when you evict everyone, to make way for your luxury doghouses."

"Yes, I can see that now," mused the Earl.

"There's just one other thing," said Lennie. "Your working dogs have left and moved on to another job. I think they were afraid they wouldn't get paid for all the work they've done."

"Oh no!" groaned the Earl. "That's all I need. It looks like you've all got what you wanted. I'll have to halt the development until I can find a new team to work with me. No evictions today then."

Lennie winked at Badger. As the Earl nodded off, Lennie picked up the Dreamcatcher they had brought back from the Zen Den and started to play with the feathers. He kept checking to see if the Earl was definitely asleep.

"What is it, Lennie? You're obviously bursting to tell me something," asked Badger

"Sssssh!" said Lennie excitedly "Don't mention a word to the Earl, but I have the most amazing news. Louie's here. He was one of the Earl's Security Dogs"

"Louie?" asked Badger.

"Yes, Louie, my brother. He finally escaped the street fights although he was badly injured. The others call him Tri-pawed."

"I'm so pleased you've met him again. So that dream about him was a really good one, eh?"

"Yes, I don't think I need the Dreamcatcher now for my nightmares, but I thought it would look pretty in my box in the lane. Now I have a home to return to."

"Indeed," said Badger, "though how we'll get the lane back to normal after all the building work, I don't know. Still, at least it's ours again, for the meantime."

Lennie trotted homewards happier than he'd been for a while, knowing that his brother would be waiting for his return.

At the old oak tree, a p-mail had just arrived from a Soraya Jafari from Persia.

Chapter Twelve

Badger had just finished his daily patrol of the lane and sniffed the freshly delivered p-mail. He grinned when he read it. The Earl would be delighted to hear this piece of news.

He ran all the way back to his garden where his cousin was still asleep.

"Doodles, wake up, wake up! Your mother has replied. She's sorry to hear about your father, but thrilled to hear from you," said Badger eagerly.

"What? What? Already? What else did she say?"

Badger caught his breath. "Wait for this. She said she now owns a worldwide chain of pooch parlours, and wants you to go over there and manage everything for her!"

"This is fantastic, Badger. Not only will I be able to see my mother, but I'll be able to earn money, which, of course, means I can pay all my dogs to rebuild your lane."

Badger sighed contentedly.

In the lane meanwhile, Lennie and Louie were deep in conversation.

"Why don't you come with me?" asked Louie.

"But I don't know the first thing about travelling?" said Lennie frowning.

"Are you kidding me? When you told me about your trip in the flying machine and your visit to the fairground and the Crystal Cave, what did you think that was, if it wasn't travelling?" said Louie, gobsmacked.

"I suppose it would be an adventure," mumbled Lennie.

"So come with me then. I've got a bit put aside. We'll call it the *Worldwide Woof Walk*. We can go to the famous Dog Alley Boutique in Seattle's Pike Place market, the Fantastic Caverns in Missouri, and Hobie Cat Beach in Puerto Rico. I'm sure there will always be a home for you here, if all else fails. What have we got to lose, Lennie?" asked Louie.

"Epic! Okay, I'm in. When do we go?"

"Tonight," said Louie confidently.

"Right, I'll go and see if Badger has a knapsack we can borrow. And erm ... I'll need to resign my role and appoint a new gang leader."

"Good luck with choosing between Pogo Paws and Pickle. I'm not sure who's worse," chuckled Louie.

As Lennie ran off to find his gang, the Earl had already begun work on the lane. He'd re-hired all his team and paid them up-to-date. They shovelled the sand back into the sandpit, filled in all the trenches with the piles of earth, re-laid all the pipes, removed the scaffolding, and even added a few extras. On the Earl's orders, they had built a spa bath, an adventure play ramp, and installed automated drinking water taps.

"Superb!" said Badger, in admiration, who was watching excitedly on the sidelines. "You didn't have to do all that, Doodles."

"Ah, but yes, my dear boy, I think I did. You've all shown me such kindness when I really didn't deserve it. And you, Badger, have reunited me with my mother. I think it's the very least I could do after all the upset I've caused."

Badger high-fived the Earl, and said: "I'm proud to be related to you again, Doodles. Of course, I'll be expecting a free nail trim and ear pluck, the next time I'm Persia-bound."

"Of course, of course. Send me a p-mail. I'm heading off now, actually," said the Earl, who smiled genuinely for the first time since he'd arrived.

Badger hugged his cousin and waved him off fondly. As he strolled back down the lane, he saw Lennie in a huddle with Pogo Paws and Pickle.

"Hello you lot. What are you up to?" asked Badger pleasantly.

"Lennie's leaving us," said Pogo Paws.

"You too?" said Badger, turning to Lennie.

"Yes, I'm leaving now with my brother. We're off to trot the globe on Lennie and Louie's *Worldwide Woof Walk*," said Lennie proudly.

"I wish you all the luck in the world, Lennie, you deserve it. But who will lead the gang while you're away?"

Pogo Paws and Pickle looked at Lennie. Lennie looked at Badger.

"Well, that's just it. I can't decide."

"Perhaps they could share the responsibility?" suggested Badger

Pogo Paws and Pickle stared at each other in horror.

"What a great idea, Badger! Yes, that's it! I hereby bestow the role of gang leader on you both. You are joint leaders. And Pogo Paws, my old box on the lane is still there if you need a break from Pickle's nagging," winked Lennie.

Pogo Paws and Pickle ran off, bickering all the way.

Badger turned to Lennie and said, "Cheerio, my friend. I'm glad your nightmares have gone, that you've met up with your brother again, and that you're heading off on a massive adventure with him. I'll miss you though."

"I'll miss you too, Badger, and thank you so much for all your help. I'll never forget that trip to the Crystal Cave. But I'll try and forget the Back of Beyond and the Dream Dodgems."

"Yes, that was the bumpiest ride I've ever had," chuckled Badger.

"At least the lane will be here, as I know and love it, when I return," added Lennie.

"Sometimes, good things have to fall apart so that better things can fall together," said Badger wisely.

Lennie left with Louie to start his new life on the road. As Badger settled down in his garden with a very well-deserved higgledy-piggledy tower of toast, he thought: *What a badgical magical job well done all round. But how on earth will Pogo Paws and Pickle lead a gang of none?*

ALSO PUBLISHED BY THE LUNICORN PRESS

Badger the Mystical Mutt
ISBN: 978-0-9569640-0-7

Badger the Mystical Mutt
and the Barking Boogie
ISBN: 978-0-9560640-1-4

www.badgerthemysticalmutt.com